DESPICABLE ME

MINION MADE

™

Published by Bendon, Inc. Printed in the U.S.A.
The BENDON name, logo, and Tear and Share are trademarks of Bendon, Inc. Ashland, OH 44805. 1-888-5 BENDON. No part of this book may be reproduced or copied in any form without written permission from the copyright owner.

UNIVERSAL
A COMCAST COMPANY

ILLUMINATION
ENTERTAINMENT

www.despicable.me

How many pictures of each can you find?

Margo:

Edith:

Agnes:

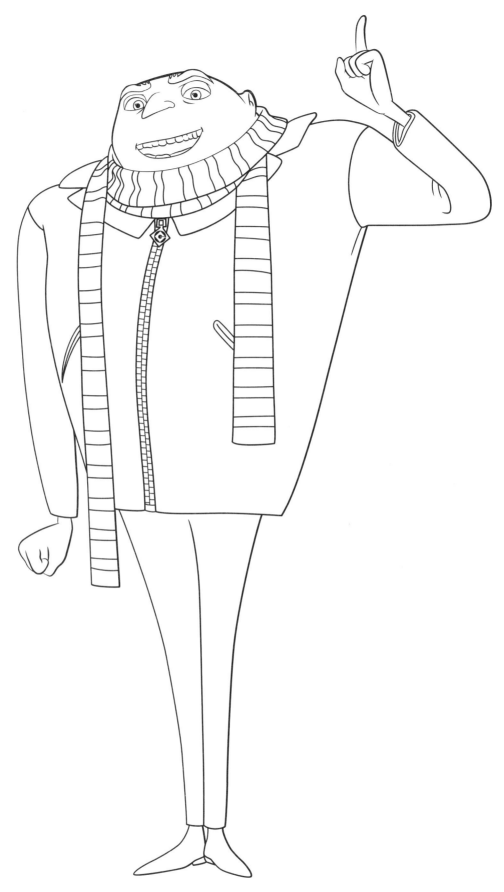

You can't handle the Gru!

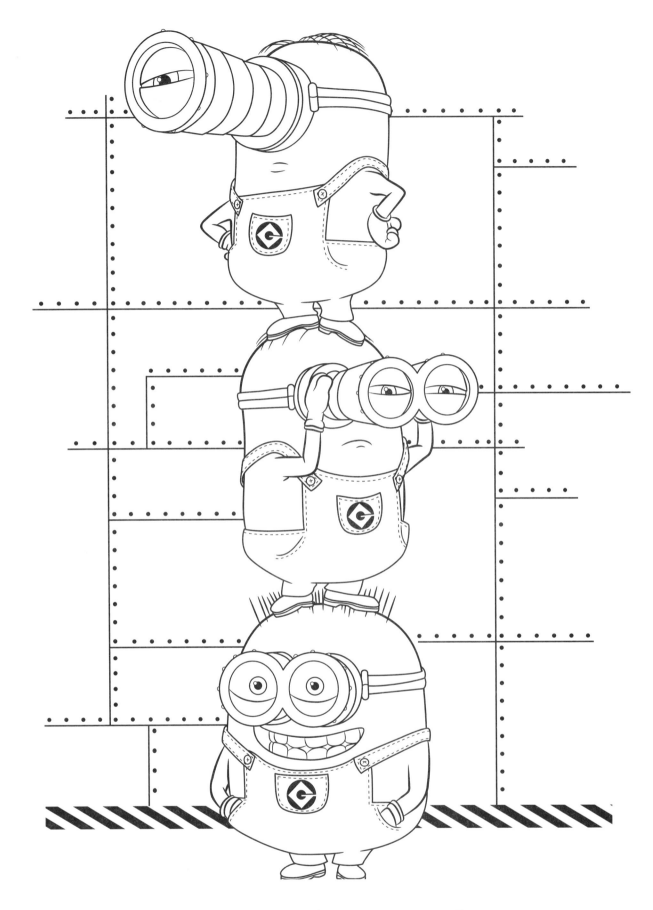

Caution: Minions at work!

Team Minion

It's good to be a Minion!

Look up, down, across, and diagonally. Help the Minions find these despicable words!

MINION
BELLO
POOPAYE
KARATE
BANANA

```
M P J I N G T H E T N
L O Q K A R U P S N O
U O C B A N A N A Q I
K P A E D R O G T I N
J A T L O T A O C G I
Z Y N L K R L T K J M
H E T O C B D U E G P
```

It's so fluffy!

There's a new Gru in town!

How many words can you make using the letters in:

DESPICABLE ME

Help Carl find the Freeze Ray and return it to Gru.

START

FINISH

One in a Minion!

I'm so bad, I'm good.

Which leads to the sundae with a cherry on top?

Answer:

Minions need love, too.

So many Minions, so little time!

One is never enough!

Eye eye, captain!

How many Minions do you count?

Your Answer:

Minions rock!

Quiet, please – test in progress.

Let's hula!

Use the grid to draw and paint Tom.

Which pieces complete the picture?

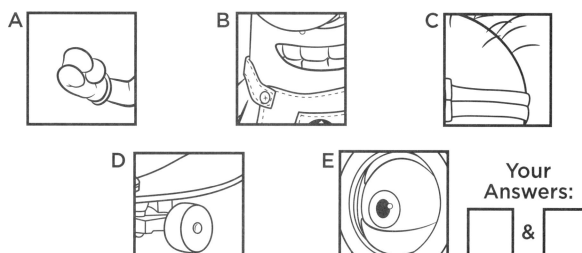

A

B

C

D

E

Your Answers:

☐ & ☐

Hug a Minion

Match the Minion to the correct shadow.

Testing 1-2-3.

Oops!

Proud to be a Minion

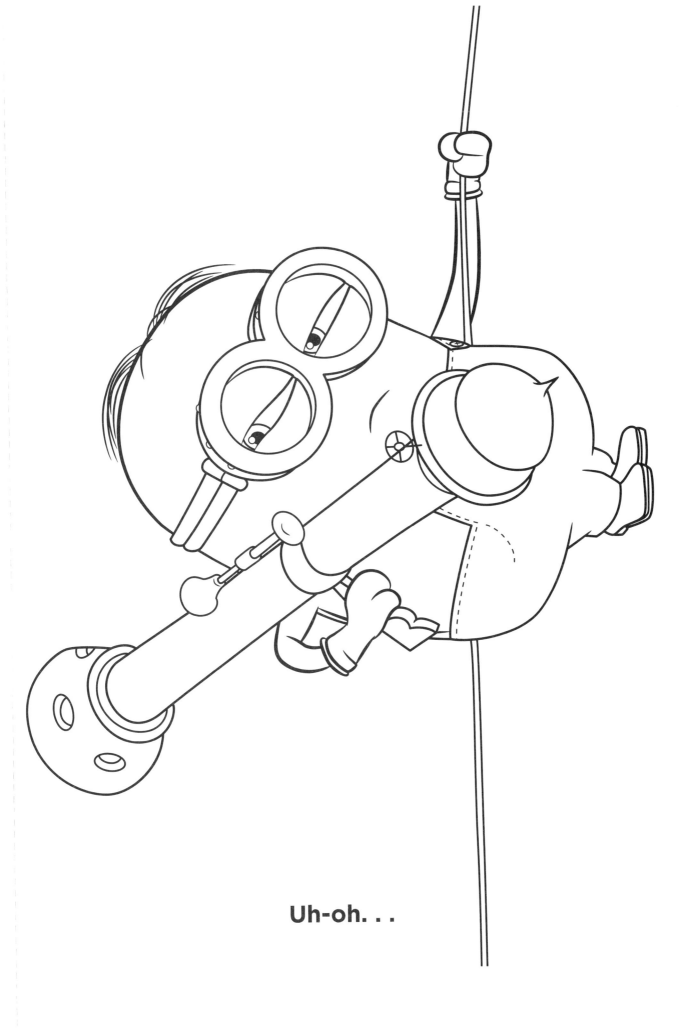

Uh-oh. . .

Think of words that start with the letters in the name Margo. Two have been done for you.

	Name	Food	Animal	Place
M				
A				
R			RHINO	
G				
O	OPAL			

Yellow is no longer mellow.

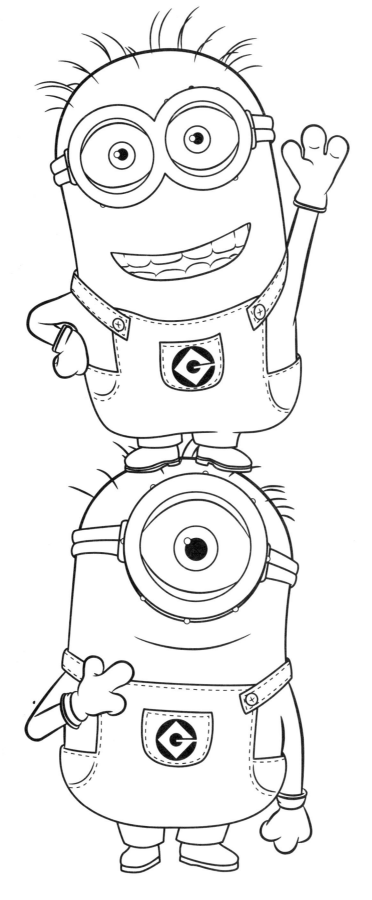

You say Goodbye and I say Yellow.

Think of words that start with the letters in the name Antonio. Three have been done for you.

	Name	Food	Animal	Place
A				
N			Newt	
T				
O				
N				
I		Iceberg Lettuce		
O	OPAL			

It's a Minion thing, you wouldn't understand.

Which pieces complete the picture?

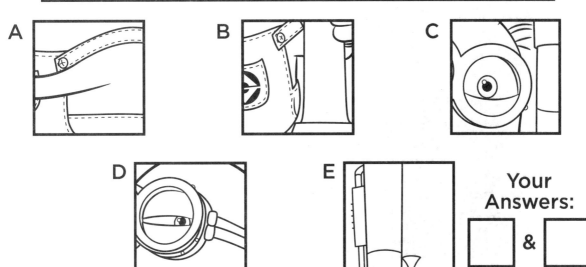

A

B

C

D

E

Your
Answers:

☐ & ☐

ANSWER: B, D

Family First

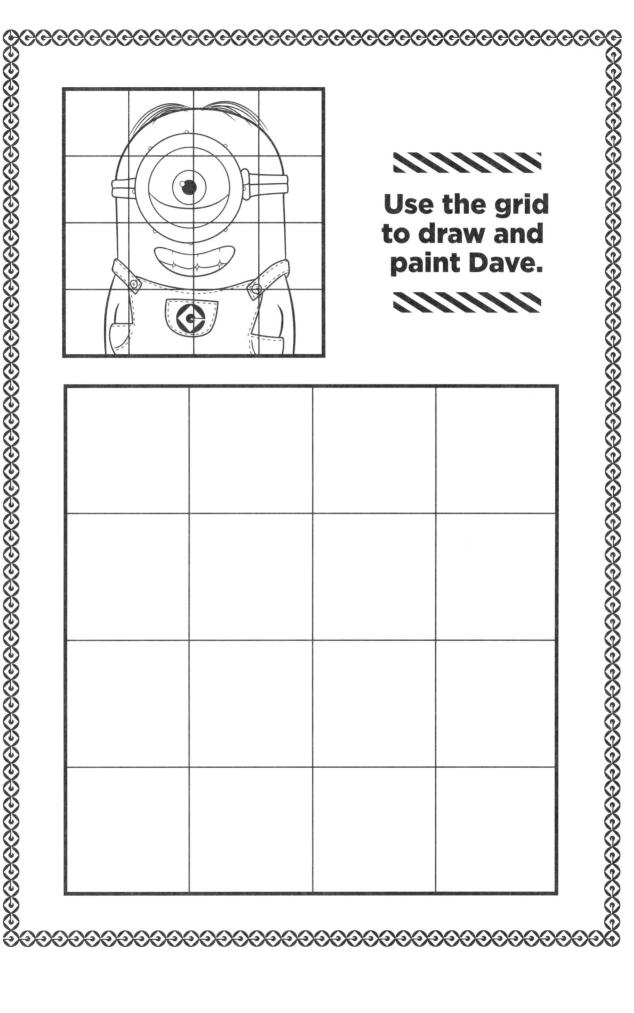

Use the grid to draw and paint Dave.

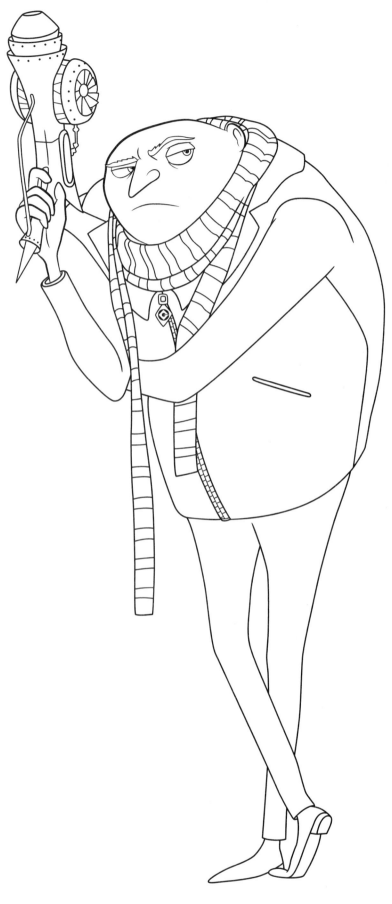

Evil 101

You say Despicable like it's a bad thing.

Thanks a Minion!

Need More Data

99% Adorable, 1% Despicable

Best. Minion. Ever.

Help Stuart find his way to Dave.

You say Poopaye! I say Bello!

Modern Minion

Failure is always an option.

So happy to spy you.

Yellow Bello!

Minion Power

Which Minion is different?

Eye-con

Proud to be a Minion!